G000129145

THE FAT OF THE LAND

Exclusive Distributors

International Music Publications Limited
Southend Road, Woodford Green, Essex IG8 8HN, England

International Music Publications Limited
25 Rue D'Hauteville, 75010 Paris, France

International Music Publications GmbH, Germany
Marstallstraße 8, D-80539 Munchen, Germany

Danmusik
Vognmagergade 7, DK-1120 Copenhagen K, Denmark

Warner/Chappell Music Australia Pty Ltd.
Talavera Road, North Ryde, New South Wales 2113, Australia

Folio © 1997 International Music Publications Ltd
Southend Road, Woodford Green, Essex IG8 8HN

Music Transcribed by Barnes Music Engraving Ltd., East Sussex TN22 4HA
Printed by The Panda Group · Haverhill · Suffolk CB9 8PR · UK
Binding by ABS · Cambridge

Reproducing this music in any form is illegal and forbidden by the Copyright,
Designs and Patents Act 1988

Photograph pages 4, 5, 32 Steve Gullick, page 12, 43 Morten Larsen

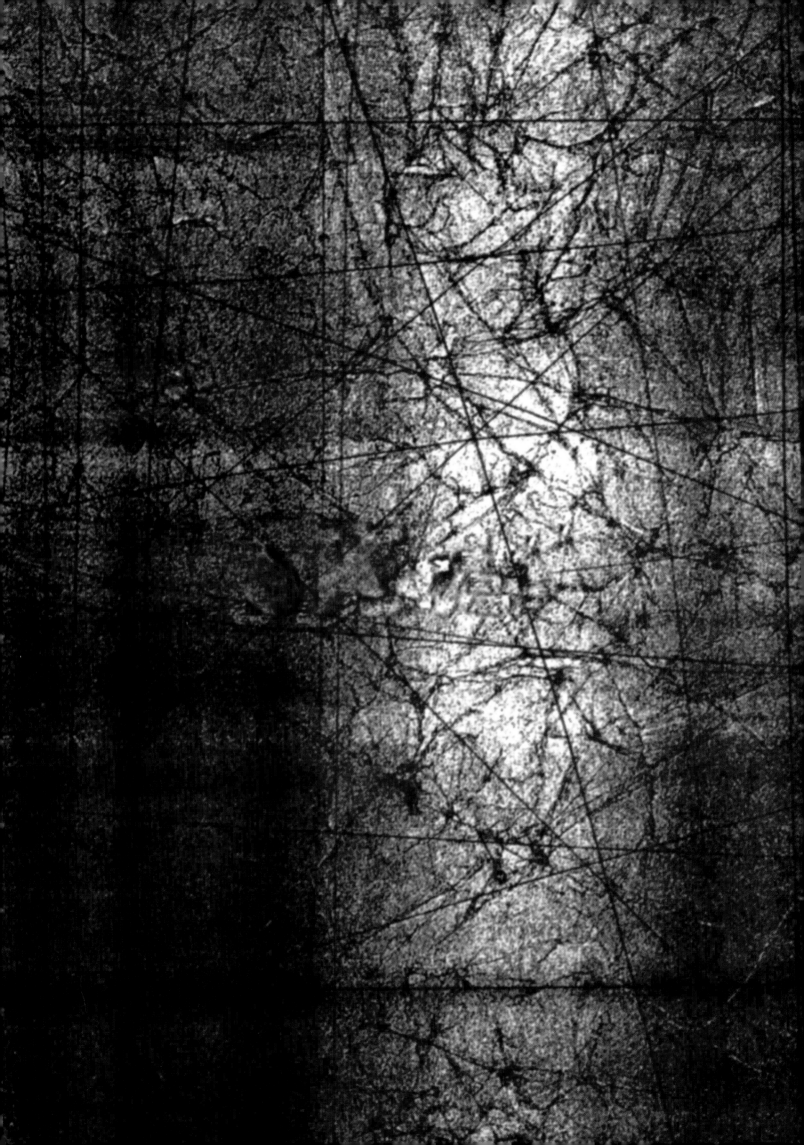

THE FAT OF THE LAND

DIESEL POWER

YO/I USED TO CHECKOUT LYRICS/AND PUMP THE FORMAT/BUILD WITH SKILL WITH
TECHNIQUE/COMPUTER ADAT/MY LYRICAL FORM/IS CLOUDS ON YOUR BRAINSTORM/I
GET HYPE/THINK THOUGHT FLOW/ACROBAT/SINK THE TRACK/PUMP THE TRACK/
TRANSMISSIONS/CLOSE LIKE SPORES/REACT PAST THESE VISIONS/AND HURRYING
MORE REFLECTS ON THE DANCEFLOOR/BLOWING UP/AND HAVING MAD PEOPLE SHOWING
UP/PACKING CROWDS/JAM-PACKED VENUES/NEEDLES COLLAPSE/WHILE
ATMOSPHERES CONTINUE/SPRINKLE THAT/WINNING LIKE THAT/MOVING LIKE THAT/
HITING LIKE THAT/THE MELODY IS FAT/YO I'M ON THE ENERGY SOURCE/THE COSMIC
BOSS/WITH PRODIGY/GIVEN ASTROLOGY/MY INTELLECTS DEVOUR/WITH DIESEL POWER

BLOWS YOUR MIND/DRASTICALLY/FANTASTICALLY

WE SPUN BACK/REWIND-DIESEL POWER/BLOWS YOUR MIND/DRASTICALLY/
FANTASTICALLY/IT HAS TO BE/AUTOMATICALLY/CHECK IT OUT/YOU BETTER WORK IT OUT
/DREAMS TO ANOTHER BOUT/MY TECHNIQUES/STRATEGIES/ABILITIES/WILL LEAVE
CORDLESS MICS/HANGING LIKE SPRING LEADS/DO A TRACK SO FAST/BEYOND FROM YOU
AND I/LYRICAL TACTICS/VOCAL GYMNASTICS/EASE AND PEPPED UP/YOU GET SWEPT UP
/SMACKED UP/BACKED UP/YOUR CREWS ALL CRACKED UP/CHECK IT SLOW/PICK
CHOOSE QUICK/YOU CAN'T STICK/MY MEDICALRANGE/IS STRANGE AS ANGLES/YOU GET
TANGLED/TWIST INSIDE A FRACTION/CHANNELS REPEAT COMPLETE/CAN"T COMPLETE
CHECK THE HOUR AND TEXTURE/MIND ADVENTURE/EMPLOIT THE POINT/INTO TRACKS/
TO DEVOUR MY INTELLECTS PROCEED/MY DIESEL POWER

BLOWS YOUR MIND/DRASTICAALY/FANTASTICALLY

BACK ATTACK THE WACK/PACK THE FAX TO ME/YOU DONT WANT NONE/HIGH-QUALITY
ACTION B/STILL STANDING/DAMAGING YOUR OTHER MANNER/QUICK REVERSE/POTENT
IAS THE FIRST VERSE MY AMPLIFIER/BLOWS ON YOUR WORLDS HIGHER/WORLDS SIRE/
CUTS LIKE A BARBED-WIRE/RECORD-PLAY/I PULL UP ON YOUR ENERGY DAY/FAST-
FORWARD/I MOVE/AND I SWING TOWARDS IT/EXIT-LOAD/PUT YOUR BRAIN IN RIGHT MODE/
SELECTIVE MIX/THE MAN WILL PERFECT THE FIX/HEADS LIGHTLY/BITE ME/COPY XEROX/
COP SAND BLOCKS/YOU CAN'T KNOCK THEM OUT THERE/I'LL KEEP LIFTING/SHIFTING/
PERSISTENT INTELLIGENT KINGPIN/GIVEN ASTROLOGY/AS I ROLL WITH PRODIGY

WITH DIESEL POWER
BLOWS YOUR MIND/DRASTICALLY/FANTASTICALLY

FUEL MY FIRE

I'VE GOT A WORD OF THANKS/THAY I'D LIKE TO SAY
FOR THE WAY THAT I FEEL/TODAY
GOT STACKS/OF CHIPS/ON MY SHOULDER
COS I MADE THE MISTAKE/OF TRUSTING YOU

PEOPLE LIKE YOU JUST FUEL MY FIRE
PEOPLE LIKE YOU JUST DO

YOU LIAR

YEAH MY LAYERS ARE THICK/AND I'VE GOT BAD ATTIDUDE

YEAH\\GOT A GRUDGE/THAT I'M HOLDING
FOR AS LONG AS I LIKE/COS YOU/RED TO MY FACE
AND THAT'S SOMETHING THAT I CAN'T FORGIVE

YOU LIAR

YEAH MY LAYERS ARE THICK/AND I'VE GOT BAD ATTIDUDE

YEAH\\GOT A GRUDGE/THAT I'M HOLDING
FOR AS LONG AS I LIKE/COS YOU/RED TO MY FACE
AND THAT'S SOMETHING THAT I CAN'T FORGIVE

FUNKY SHIT

OH MY GOD/THATS SOME FUNKY SHIT

FIRESTARTER

I'M THE TROUBLE STARTER - PUNKING INSTIGATOR
I'M THE FEAR ADDICTED/DANGER ILLUSTRATED
I'M A FIRESTARTER/TWISTED FIRESTARTER
YOU'RE THE FIRESTARTER/TWISTED FIRESTARTER
I'M THE BITCH YOU HATED/FILTH INFATUATED
I'M THE PAIN YOU TASTED/FELL INTOXICATED
I'M THE SELF-INFLICTED/PUNK DETONATOR
I'M THE ONE INVENTED/TWISTED ANIMATOR

NARAYAN

IF YOU BELIEVE/THE WESTERN SUN/IS FALLING DOWN/ON EVERYONE
YOURE BEAKING FREE/AND THE MORNINGS COME/IF YOU WOULD KNOW/YOUR TIME HAS COME

I FEEL IT
I FEEL ANOTHER ENERGY/I FEEL A POWER GROWING

OM/NAMA/NARAYANA

BREATHE

BREATHE WITH ME
BREATHE THE PRESSURE/COME PLAY MY GAME/I'LL TEST YA
PSYCHO-SOMATIC/ATIC-INSANE
COME PLAY MY GAME
INHALE/INHALE YOU'RE THE VICTIM
COME PLAY MY GAME
EXHALE,EXHALE EXHALE

SMACK MY BITCH UP

CHANGE MY PITCH UP/SMACK MY BITCH UP

MINDFIELDS

THIS IS DANGEROUS/OPEN UP YOUR HEAD/FEEL THE SHELLSHOCK
THIS IS DANGEROUS/I WALK THROUGH MINEFIELDS/AND WATCH YOUR HEAD ROCK

SERIAL THRILLA

DAMAGE DESTRUCTOR/CROWD DISRUPTOR/YOUTH-CORRUPTOR/EVERYTIMER DAMAGE
DESTRUCTOR/CROWD DISRUPTOR/MAINLINER/EVERYTIMER

THE FAT OF THE LAND

The Prodigy released their third album **The Fat Of The Land** on June 30th 1997. The album features 10 tracks:

Smack My Bitch Up
The phrase "Change My Pitch Up / Smack My Bitch Up" is sampled from "Give The Drummer Some" by Ultramagnetic MCs which can be found on their first LP "Critical Beatdown." The Indian vocal was performed by Shahin Bada.

Breathe
Originally released as a single in November 1996, "Breathe" is The Prodigy's biggest selling single to date. Vocals are supplied by both Maxim and Keith, guitar by long time Prodigy collaborator Jim Davies.

Diesel Power
Rapping by Kool Keith, formerly of Ultramagnetic MCs, who recorded a critically acclaimed LP for Mo' Wax last year as Dr Octagon.

Funky Shit
Builds around a Beastie Boys sample, from "Root Down" on Ill Communication.

Serial Thrilla
Vocal by Keith.

Mindfields
Vocal by Maxim.

Narayan
Recorded in collaboration with Crispin Mills of Kula Shaker, who provided vocals and lyrics.

Firestarter
Released as a single in March 1996. "Firestarter" was Number One for three weeks in the UK. It was the first Prodigy recording to feature Keith's vocals.

Climbatize
A purely instrumental track.

Fuel My Fire
A cover version - the original is by all-girl LA punk band L7. Keith provides vocals, assisted by Saffron from Republica.

SMACK MY BITCH UP

Words and Music by
Liam Howlett, Cedric Miller, Trevor Randolph,
Trevor Smith, Keith Thornton

Change my pitch up, smack my bitch up.

Change my pitch up, smack my bitch up.

© 1997 EMI Virgin Music Ltd, London WC2H 0EA
London Music Ltd, London W4 4HS

Smack my bitch up.

Yeah

Ah

Ah

Yeah

BREATHE

Words by Liam Howlett, Keith Palmer and Keith Flint
Music by Liam Howlett

♩ = 126

Capo 1

Instrumental

sim.

Breathe with me.

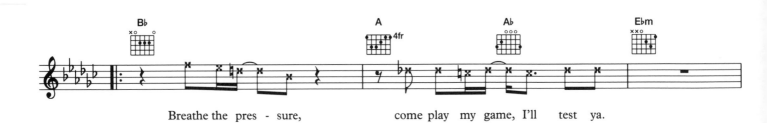

Breathe the pres - sure, come play my game, I'll test ya.

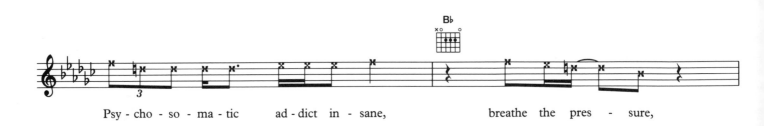

Psy - cho - so - ma - tic ad - dict in - sane, breathe the pres - sure,

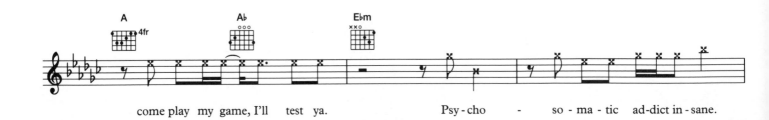

come play my game, I'll test ya. Psy - cho - so - ma - tic ad - dict in - sane.

© 1996 EMI Virgin Music Limited, London WC2H 0EA
MCA Music Ltd, London W6 8JA

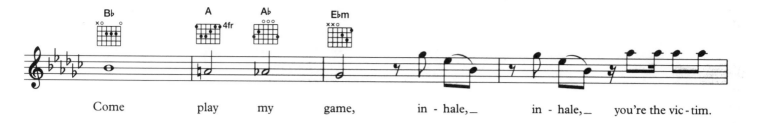

Come play my game, in - hale,__ in - hale,__ you're the vic - tim.

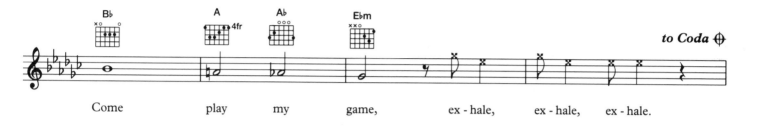

to Coda

Come play my game, ex - hale, ex - hale, ex - hale.

Instrumental

sim.

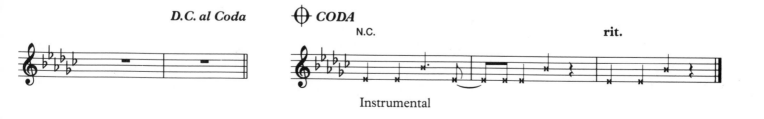

D.C. al Coda   **CODA**   *rit.*

N.C.

Instrumental

DIESEL POWER

Words and Music by
Liam Howlett and Kool Keith

♩ = 112
[C]

Yo!

I used to check out ly-rics, and pump the for - mat, build with skill__ with tech-nique, com-pu -ter A - DAT,

my ly - ri -cal form is clouds on your brain-storm, I get hype, think thought flow, a - cro-bat,

sink the track, pump the track, trans - mis - sions,__ close like__ spores, re - act past soul vi-sions,

and hur - ry-ing more re-flects on the dance - floor, blow-ing up, and hav-ing mad peo-ple

© 1996 EMI Virgin Music Ltd, London WC2H 0EA
Momentum Music Ltd, London SW18 1AA

show-ing up, pack - ing crowds, jam-packed ven-ues, need-les col - lapse, while at - mos - pheres con -

- ti -nue, to sprin-kle that, win-ning like that, mov-ing like that,_ hit-ting like that, the me - lo - dy is

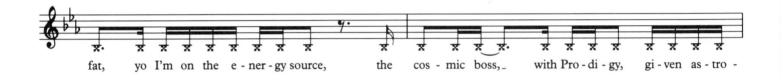

fat, yo I'm on the e - ner -gy source, the cos - mic boss,_ with Pro - di - gy, gi - ven as - tro -

- lo - gy, my in -tel -lects de - vo - ur, with die - sel_ pow - er.

Blows your mind_ dras - tic - ally, fan - tas - tic - ally.

Blows your mind_ dras - tic - ally, fan - tas - tic - ally.

Blows your mind_ dras - tic - ally, fan - tas - tic - ally.

Blows your mind_ dras - tic - ally, fan - tas-

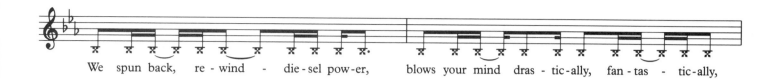

We spun back, re - wind – die - sel pow - er, blows your mind dras - tic - ally, fan - tas - tic - ally,

it has to be au - to - ma - ti - cally, check it out, you bet - ter work it out, change to an - oth - er bout,

my tech - niques, stra - te - gies,_ a - bi - li - ties, will leave cord - less mics, hang - ing like spring leads,

do a track so fast,_ be - yond from you and I, ly - ri - cal tac - tics, vo - cal gym - nas - tics,

ease and pepped up you get swept up, smacked up, backed up, your crews all cracked up,

check it slow,_ pick choose quick, you can't stick, my me - di - cal range, is strange as an - gles,

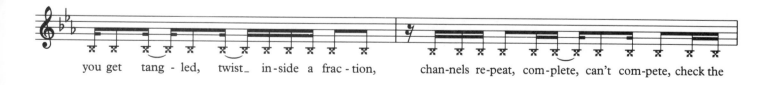

you get tang - led, twist_ in - side a frac - tion, chan - nels re - peat, com - plete, can't com - pete, check the

ho - ur, tex - ture, mind ad - ven - ture, ex - ploit___ the point, in - to tracks, to de -

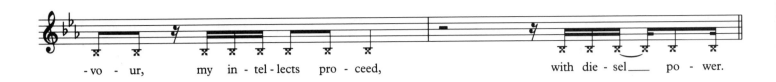

-vo - ur, my in - tel - lects pro - ceed, with die - sel__ po - wer.

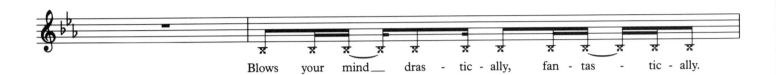

Blows your mind__ dras - tic - ally, fan - tas - tic - ally.

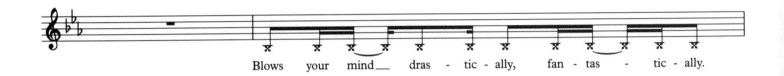

Blows your mind__ dras - tic - ally, fan - tas - tic - ally.

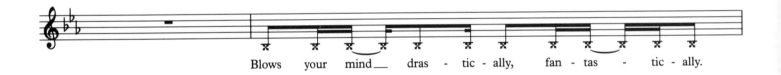

Blows your mind__ dras - tic - ally, fan - tas - tic - ally.

Blows your mind__ dras - tic - ally, fan - tas-

Back at - tack__ the wack, pack the fax__ to me, you don't want none, high-qua - li - ty ac - tion, B,

still stand-ing, da - mag-ing your oth - er man-ner, quick re-verse, po -tent as the first verse,

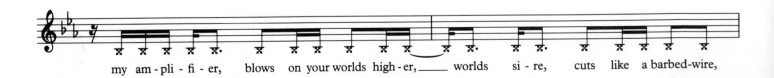

my am - pli - fi - er, blows on your worlds high - er,__ worlds si - re, cuts like a barbed-wire,

re-cord play,_ I pull up on you ev-ery day, fast-for-ward, I move, and I swing to-wards,

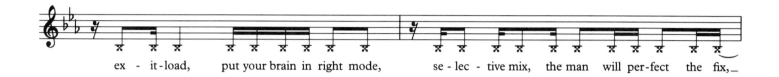

ex - it -load, put your brain in right mode, se - lec - tive mix, the man will per-fect the fix,_

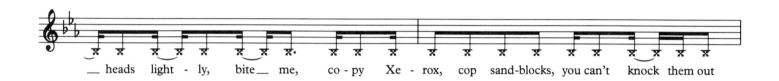

_ heads light - ly, bite_ me, co - py Xe - rox, cop sand-blocks, you can't knock them out

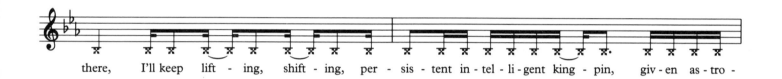

there, I'll keep lift - ing, shift - ing, per - sis - tent in - tel - li - gent king - pin, giv-en as-tro -

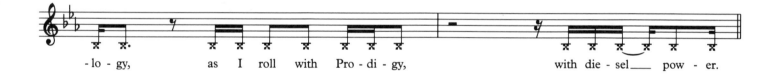

- lo - gy, as I roll with Pro - di - gy, with die - sel_ pow - er.

Blows your mind_ dras - tic - ally, fan - tas - tic - ally.

Blows your mind_ dras - tic - ally, fan - tas - tic - ally.

Blows your mind_ dras - tic - ally, fan - tas - tic - ally.

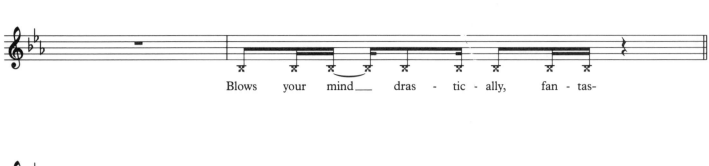

Blows your mind___ dras - tic-ally, fan - tas-

Mo - no sev - en oh six eight oh_____ sev - en three four twen - ty - one

ro - bot__ son-ic.

Blows your mind___ dras - tic - ally, fan - tas - tic - ally.

Blows your mind___ dras - tic - ally, fan - tas - tic - ally.

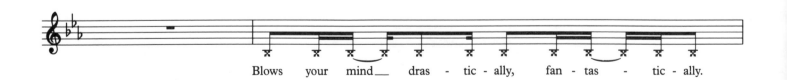

Blows your mind___ dras - tic - ally, fan - tas - tic - ally.

Blows your mind___ dras - tic - ally, fan - tas - tic - ally.

FUNKY SHIT

Words and Music by
Liam Howlett, Michael Diamond,
Adam Yauch, Adam Horovitz

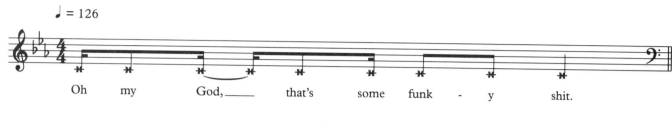

Oh my God, _____ that's some funk - y shit.

[C]

play 3 times

play 3 times

Oh my God, that's some funk - y shit.

© 1997 EMI Virgin Music Ltd, London WC2H 0EA
PolyGram Music Publishing Ltd, London W4 4HS

20

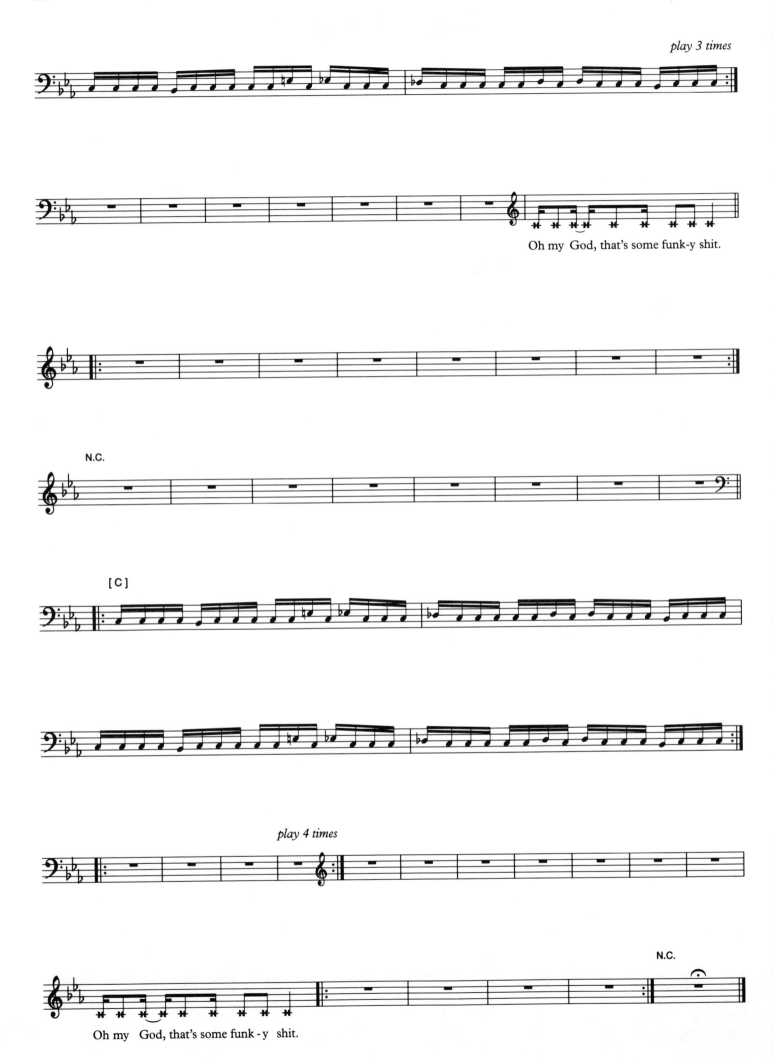

play 3 times

Oh my God, that's some funk-y shit.

N.C.

[C]

play 4 times

N.C.

Oh my God, that's some funk-y shit.

SERIAL THRILLA

Words and Music by
Liam Howlett, Keith Flint,
Skin and Len Arran

© 1997 EMI Virgin Music Ltd, London WC2H 0EA
MCA Music Ltd, London W6 8JA
Chrysalis Music Ltd, London W10 6SP

Se - ri - al thril - la, se - ri-ous kil - ler. Se - ri - al thril - la,

se - ri-ous kil - ler. Se - ri - al thril - la, se - ri-ous kil - ler.

Se - ri-al thril-la, se - ri-ous kil-ler.

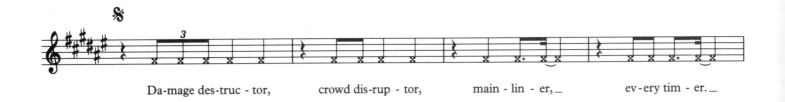

Da-mage des-truc - tor, crowd dis-rup - tor, main - lin - er, __ ev - ery tim - er. __

Taste me, __ taste me, __ suc-cumb to me, __ suc-cumb to me. __

Se - ri - al thril - la, se - ri-ous kil - ler. Se - ri - al thril - la,

se - ri-ous kil - ler. Se - ri - al thril - la, se - ri-ous kil - ler.

to Coda ✛

Se - ri - al thril - la, se - ri-ous kil-ler.

play 6 times

D.§ al Coda

✛ *CODA*

LIAM HOWLETT · MAXIM REALITY · KEITH FLINT · LEEROY THORNHILL

Glastonbury, June 1995. It's getting dark, and the field in front of the NME stage is heaving from front to back as searchlights sweep the crowd and discordant samples echo through the air. Maxim Reality strides to the edge of the stage, and stares into the night with crazy white eyes. He raises his microphone. "Glastonbury ... Are you ready to rock ?" As the shattered glass breakbeats of **Break And Enter** ring out at huge volume and thousands of dancing people turn the entire field into one enormous moshpit, the crowd are greeted by the deranged spectacle of a flame haired Keith Flint rolling onto the stage in a massive glass ball. There was no more room for doubt – The Prodigy's state-of-the-art fusion of dance energy, rock power, and visual madness had arrived.

Glastonbury must have seemed a universe away back in 1990, when Liam Howlett arrived at the offices of XL Recordings with a demo cassette of ten tunes that he'd recorded in his bedroom. But those raw, edgy tracks, taking inspiration from the hard end of the underground dance scene (Joey Beltram, Meat Beat Manifesto) and combining those sounds with speeded-up hip-hop breakbeats, were innovative and exciting enough to secure him a record deal – and four of them were lifted direct from the tape to make up The Prodigy's first single. **What Evil Lurks** was released on vinyl only in February 1991, selling a respectable 7000 copies and gathering The Prodigy's first few mentions in the dance press at the same time. It was a promising enough beginning, but the next single was a whole different story.

Charly was the record that propelled The Prodigy out of the underground rave scene and into the Top 3. It had been *the* buzz record on the party scene for months before its commercial release, and it flew out of the shops as soon as it was available. Looking back, past the dismal spate of cash-in kiddy techno records that followed in *Charly's* wake (Roobarb, The Magic Roundabout and Sesame Street all received the cheesy breakbeat treatment), it's hard to remember just how important a tune it was for the time. It captured the euphoria, the energy, the sense of humour, and the shared excitement of being part of a massive underground adventure – meeting at motorway service stations to call up mobile phones and follow coded directions before dancing all night in bizarre locations was a weekly ritual for thousands and thousands of people back then, and rave, which now sounds like a dirty word, was the biggest and best thing to happen to British culture since punk rock.

No band epitomised the relentless energy of rave culture better than The Prodigy – with *Charly* causing whistle posse madness around the country, there was no shortage of promoters willing to put on the band's frenetic live show, and from the very beginning they toured incessantly. Leeroy's lurching grace, Maxim's incendiary mic style and Keith's evident insanity were all part of the appeal – without them, The Prodigy would have been just one more faceless keyboard act, but with them they were an exhilarating whirl of on- stage madness. The band quickly built up a devoted fanbase within the rave scene – and earned a reputation (which they have never relinquished) as the best buzz going. These fans propelled *Charly* into the Top Ten when it was commercially released, and exposed The Prodigy to the mainstream for the first time. Despite the snobbish derision that the dance press started to direct towards the band because of their commercial success (Mixmag famously put a picture of Liam pointing a gun at his head on the front cover, accompanied by the headline "Did Charly Kill Rave ?"), the rave crews remained loyal, and sent a succession of records – **Everybody In The Place, Fire, Out Of Space,** and **Wind It Up** – into the upper echelons of the charts. An album, **Experience** provided seventy minutes of mayhem, and disproved the conventional wisdom of the time – which claimed that dance albums did not sell – by going gold within weeks of its release and spending 25 weeks in the Top 40.

Behind this seamless success, however, a more complicated situation was developing. By the time that **Wind It Up** made Number 11 in March 1993, the underground network of parties and events that gave birth to the band and carried it to national prominence had started to fragment. The forces of progressive house and intelligent techno were on the march, mellowing out the less committed rave kids, and driving the breakbeat diehards into the ever-faster, ever-darker maelstrom of hardcore. At the same time, Liam had grown tired of the breakbeat-plus-sample-equals-rave-anthem school of music making, and although Prodigy records continued to be successful, he no longer found them challenging to make. Rave audiences, fuelled by ecstasy, were uncritical and undemanding – they made it too easy for him to repeat himself. It was time for a change.

Displaying the kind of courage and creativity rarely shown by successful artists mining a lucrative musical niche, Liam began to take The Prodigy into uncharted territory. Live, the band concentrated less on preaching to the converted, and began to put themselves in front of less malleable audiences – they played students' unions, rock venues and festivals, increasingly excited by the more aggressive mood of crowds where alcohol was the drug of choice. Liam started listening to the hard rock music of Nirvana, Smashing Pumpkins and The Red Hot Chilli Peppers, checking out the intense live energy of Rage Against The Machine and Biohazard at festivals. Inevitably, Prodigy music started to reflect these new influences, as well as the changes happening in dance music at the time.

The transitional record was **One Love**, which made its first appearance as an anonymous white label stamped "Earthbound". A tightly syncopated mesh of tribal house music and distorted beats, the record was favourably received despite the fact that nobody knew who had made it – and when it was properly released as a Prodigy record in the summer of 1993, it fared just as well in the charts as the rave anthems that had preceded it. **One Love** was an important hurdle – the band's fans were clearly prepared to follow them through daunting changes in direction, and knowing this gave Liam the confidence to push against the boundaries of his music. From One Love onwards, Prodigy records would become more and more challenging – and more and more successful.

For twelve months after **One Love**, the Prodigy were silent – Liam was busy in the studio, working on **Music For The Jilted Generation**, the band's second album. When they broke silence, it was with their most effective record to date – **No Good (Start The Dance)**. The single combined hammering, syncopated beats, an incredibly taut bassline and chunks of screaming machine noise, all of which was barely concealed by the most immediate, radio-friendly vocal hook of the band's career. The record spent seven weeks in the Top Ten, peaking at Number 4, and paving the way for the release of the album.

Music For The Jilted Generation was released in July 1994. It went straight into the album charts at Number 1, going gold within a week of its release. And by this time the band had clearly won over the critics as well as the public – **Music For The Jilted Generation** was universally well received in the music press, and was nominated later in the year for the prestigious Mercury Music Prize. Two more singles were released from the album – **Voodoo People**, backed with a murderous mix from the then rapidly-emerging Dust Brothers (soon to become the Chemical Brothers), and **Poison**, a bruising, downtempo hip-hop instrumental which remains one of the most extreme – and popular- tracks the band have recorded. Both singles charted high despite the fact that they were already available on the album – **Poison** became the band's ninth consecutive Top 15 single.

The Prodigy's Glastonbury appearance that summer marked them out as undeniably the most exciting live band in the country – five years of practically incessant touring had clearly honed their abilities as performers. Keith, sporting dyed and shaved hair, a pierced septum, and an increasingly exotic wardrobe had become magnetically photogenic, and Maxim's cats-eye contact lenses, bare chest and daring selection of kilts were not far behind. Emboldened by their success at the best festival in Europe, the band seemed determined to play at all the others, and over the next twelve months their touring became even more relentless – Iceland, Japan, Australia, America and even Macedonia all featured on an increasingly hectic schedule. Caught up in the whirl of activity, Liam only managed occasional spells in the studio, but the time he spent there was productive to say the least – the result was The Prodigy's most incendiary musical statement to date, and the record that took them to a whole new level of success.

In March 1996, **Firestarter** entered the UK charts at Number 1. It was the band's first Number 1 single, and it stayed at the top for 3 weeks. A high- impact compound of relentless sub-bass, eerily circling guitar samples and unmistakably punk vocals, it's the most extreme, noisy and confrontational record ever to make it to the top spot – a fact not lost on the tabloids who began a witty, intelligent and well-informed "Ban This Sick Record" campaign. The video, which somehow managed to match the intensity of the music, brought Keith in all his glory to the nation for the first time, and, unsurprisingly, provoked record numbers of complaints from Top Of The Pops viewers. As a statement of intent, it was as uncompromising as it was successful.

The summer of 1996 saw The Prodigy back on the festival circuit, playing at Brighton, Phoenix, T In The Park and Reading in the UK and many more abroad. In all, The Prodigy did 70 gigs in 1996, playing to hundreds of thousands of people all over the world. Spiky-haired guitar terrorist Giz Butt joined the live show, adding to the on-stage mayhem. With the band averaging a gig every five days, as well as spending hours in airports and hotels, it's perhaps not surprising that the third album took so long to record.

In November, **Breathe** became the band's second single of the year, and their second Number 1. Keith and Maxim growled their way through a ferocious call-and-response chorus, while Liam piled on the distortion and pulled a few deft tricks with a moody acoustic guitar. **Breathe** quickly outsold even **Firestarter**, becoming The Prodigy's first ever platinum single (over 700,000 copies sold in the UK) and establishing them once and for all in the premier league of British bands. Abroad, the touring was evidently paying off – **Breathe** was a top 20 hit in more than 20 countries, making it to Number 1 in 8 of them. The single has sold well over 1.5 million copies worldwide.

In the Spring of 1997, with Firestarter making its tenacious way up the US Billboard Top 100, The Prodigy released their third album on June 30th, the title being **The Fat Of The Land**. As well as **Breathe** and **Firestarter**, this album features a collaboration with Crispin Mills from Kula Shaker, and a track called **Diesel Power** with wayward lyrical madman Kool Keith, also known as Doctor Octagon. The album also features new tracks featuring vocals by Keith and Maxim.

MINDFIELDS

Words and Music by
Liam Howlett

This is dan - ge-rous, op - en up_ your head, feel the shell-

- shock. This is dan - ge-rous,

I walk through mine - fields and watch your head_ rock.

This is dan-

- ge-rous, op - en up_ your head, feel the shell - shock.

© 1996 EMI Virgin Music Ltd, London WC2H 0EA

This is dan - ge-rous,   op - en up__ your head, feel your shell-

- shock.   This is dan - ge-rous,

I walk through mine-fields and watch your head__ rock.   This is dan-

I watch your head rock.

This is dan -

- ge-rous,

op - en up__ your head, feel the shell - shock.

This is dan - ge-rous,

op - en up__ your head, feel the shell-

- shock.

This is dan - ge-rous,

1.

I walk through mine-fields and watch your head__ rock.

This is dan-

2.

B♭

play 8 times

Shell - shock.

I walk through mine-fields, I watch your head rock,

I walk through mine-fields and watch your head

F7

__ rock.

Shell - shock.

NARAYAN

Words and Music by
Liam Howlett and Crispin Mills

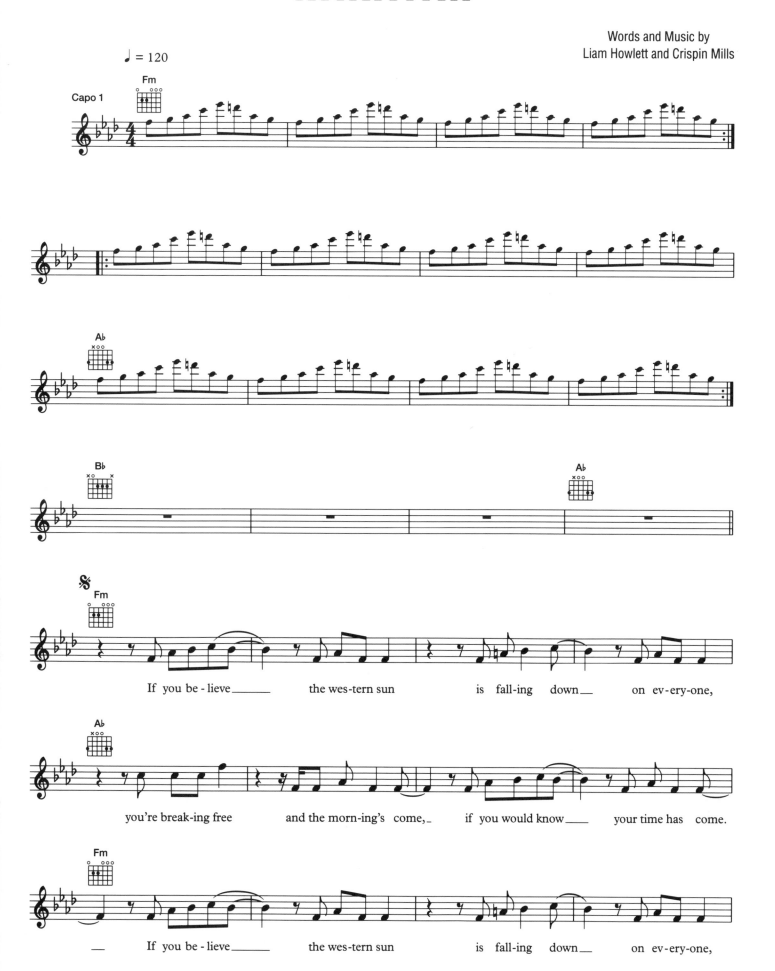

If you be-lieve _____ the wes-tern sun is fall-ing down __ on ev-ery-one,

you're break-ing free and the morn-ing's come, _ if you would know _____ your time has come.

__ If you be-lieve _____ the wes-tern sun is fall-ing down __ on ev-ery-one,

© 1997 EMI Virgin Music Ltd, London WC2H 0EA

Hit & Run Music (Publishing) Ltd, London SW3 2ND

play 9 times

Om na-ma na-ra-ya-na. Om na-ma na-ra-ya-na.

I feel an-oth-er e-ner-gy,_____ and I feel a po-wer grow-ing,__

I feel an-oth-er e-ner-gy,_____ and I feel a po-wer grow-ing._____

play 6 times [F]

play 4 times

play 4 times

segue

FIRESTARTER

Words & Music by
Liam Howlett, Keith Flint, Kim Deal, Trevor Horn, Anne Dudley,
Jonathan Jeczalik, Paul Morley & Gary Langan

© 1996 EMI Virgin Music Limited, London WC2H 0EA
MCA Music Ltd, London W6 8JA
Unforgettable Songs Limited, London W11 1DG
Perfect Songs Limited, London W11 1DG
Zomba Songs Inc., Zomba Music Publications Limited, London NW10 25G

Verse 2:
I'm the bitch you hated
Filth infactuated
I'm the pain you tasted
Fell intoxicated.

Verse 3:
I'm the self-inflicted
Mind detonator
I'm the one infected
Twisted animator.

CLIMBATIZE

Words and Music by
Liam Howlett and Tim Taylor

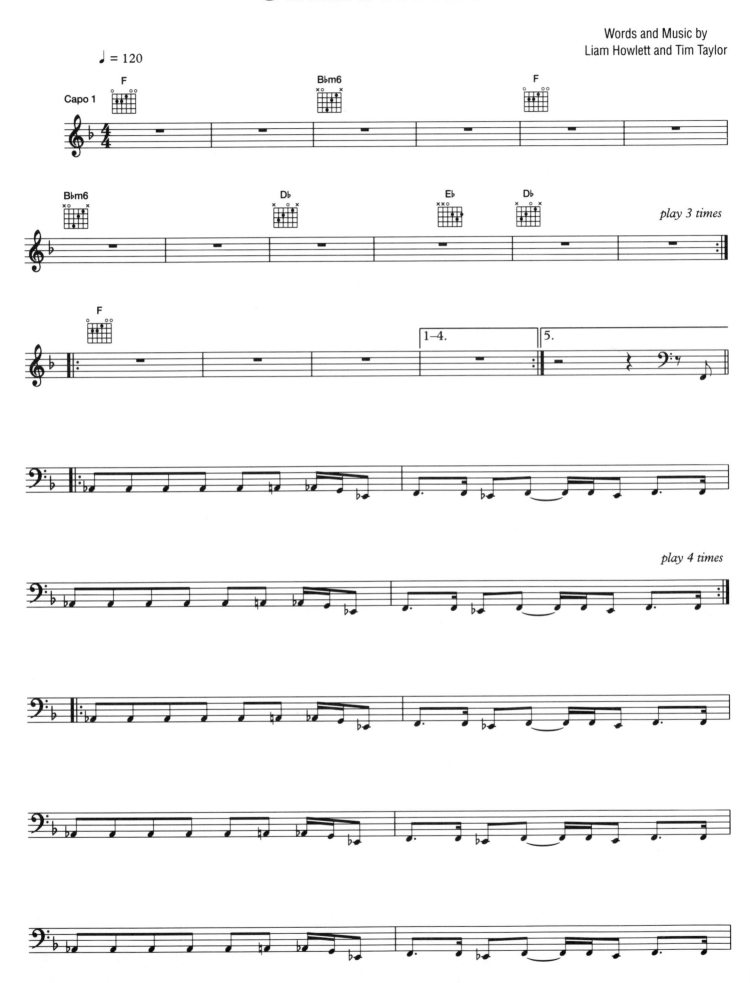

© 1997 EMI Virgin Music Ltd, London WC2H 0EA
Northcott Music, R & E Music Ltd, London E4 6PD

FUEL MY FIRE

Words and Music by
Donita Sparks and The Cosmic Psychos

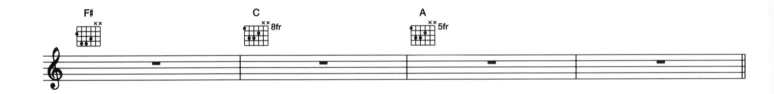

I've got a word of thanks, thanks that I'd like to say,_____
Yeah, my la - yers are thick, and I've got a bad at - ti - tude,_____

for_____ the rage that I feel,____ the rage that I feel to - day._
yeah_____ got ~ in my side___ cos these are things that I long to do._

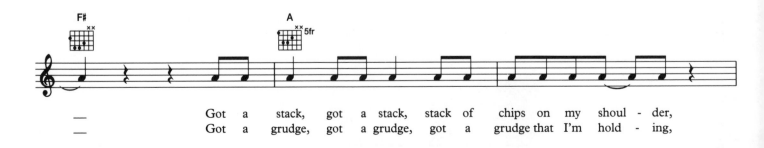

_ Got a stack, got a stack, stack of chips on my shoul - der,
_ Got a grudge, got a grudge, got a grudge that I'm hold - ing,

© 1994 Zomba Music Publishers Ltd, London NW10 2SG
Copyright Control

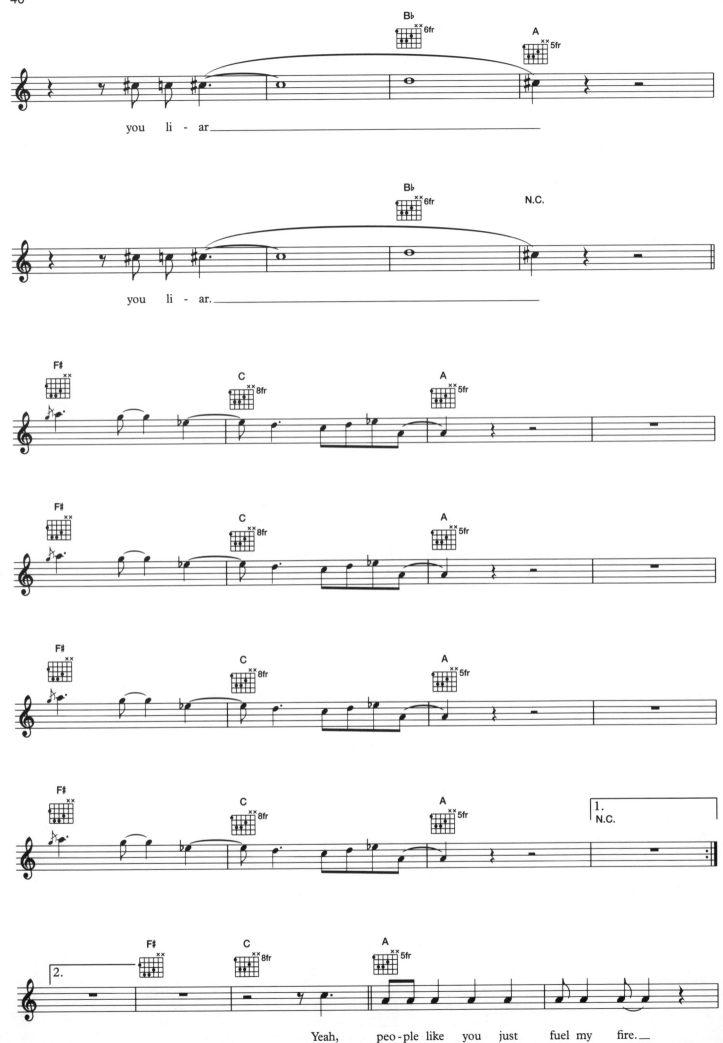

you li - ar _____

you li - ar. _____

Yeah,   peo-ple like   you   just   fuel my   fire. __

DISCOGRAPHY

SINGLES

2/91	what evil lurks	dance chart - 31
8/91	charly	dancechart - 1 national chart - 3
12/91	everybody in the place	dance chart -1 national chart - 2
9/92	fire (deleted afteroneweek)	dance chart - 1 national chart -11
11/92	out of space	dance chart - 6 national chart - 3
3/93	wind it up	dancechart - 11 national chart - 3
7/93	one love	dance chart - 5 national chart - 8
5/94	no good (start the dance)	dance chart - 4 national chart - 4
8/94	voodoo people	dance chart - 6 national chart - 13
3/95	poison	dance chart - 5 national chart - 13
3/96	firestarter	dance chart - 2 national chart -1
11/96	breathe	dance chart - 2 national chart - 1

ALBUMS

11/92	experience	dance chart - 1 national chart - 12
7/94	music for the jilted generation	dance chart - 1 national chart - 1
6/97	the fat of the land	dance chart - 1 national chart - 1

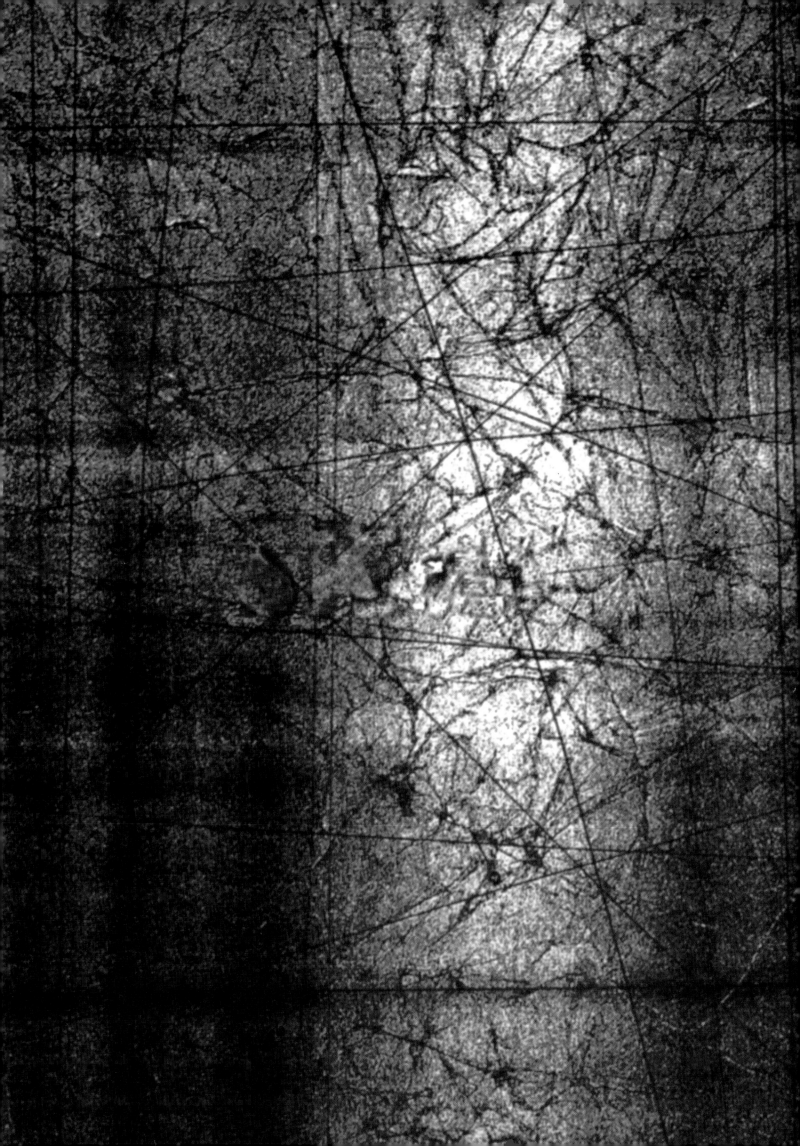